Piano • Vocal • Guitar

American Folksongs & Spirituals

75 Songs of the American Heritage

HAL•LEONARD®
CORPORATION

7777 W. BLUEMOUND RD. P.O. BOX 13819 MILWAUKEE, WI 53213

American Folksongs & Spirituals

Contents

Folksongs

Spirituals

ALL THE PRETTY LITTLE HORSES

Southeastern American Folksong

ARKANSAS TRAVELER

Southern American Folksong

Hoe-down

ANIMAL FAIR

American Folksong

Brightly, in 2 (♩. = 1 beat)

I went to the an - i - mal fair, _____ the birds and the beasts were there. _____ The big ba - boon by the light of the moon was

AURA LEE

Words by W.W. FOSDIC
Music by GEORGE R. POULTO
First published in 18

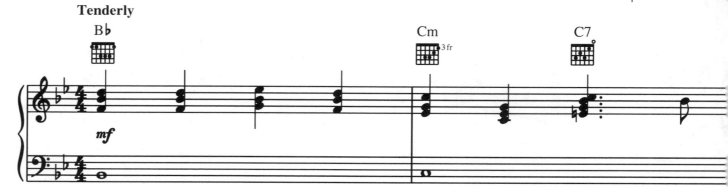

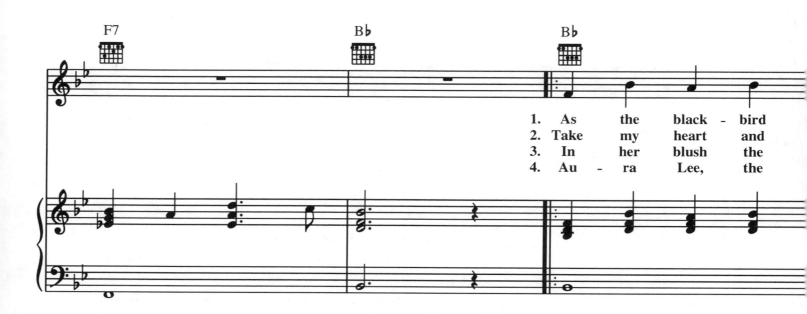

1. As the black - bird
2. Take my heart and
3. In her blush and the
4. Au - ra Lee, the

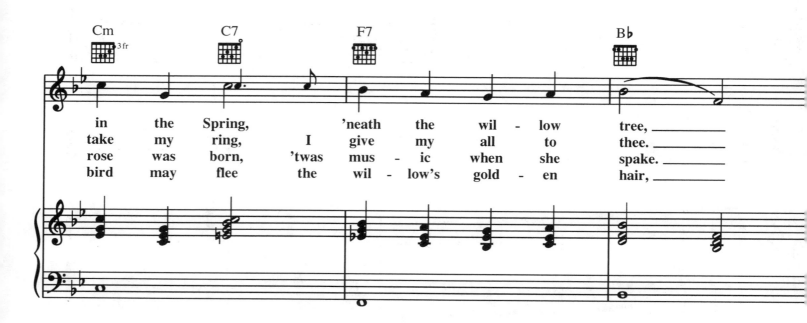

in the Spring, 'neath the wil - low tree, _____
take my ring, I give my all to thee. _____
rose was born, 'twas mus - ic when she spake. _____
bird may flee the wil - low's gold - en hair, _____

BLACK IS THE COLOR OF MY TRUE LOVE'S HAIR

Southern Appalachian Folksong

Black, black, black is the col-or of my true love's hair.

1. Her lips _____ are like a
2. Her face _____ is some-thing
3. A - lone, _____ my life would

BLOW THE CANDLES OUT

American Folksong

THE BLUE TAIL FLY
(JIMMY CRACK CORN)

Folk version o*
minstrel song by DAN EMMET*
(Emmett's song w*
first published in 184*

THE BOLL WEEVIL

Texas Folksong, c. 189

BUFFALO GALS
(WON'T YOU COME OUT TONIGHT?)

Words and Music
COOL WHITE (JOHN HODGE
First published 184

BURY ME NOT ON THE LONE PRAIRIE

Cowboy Ballad, c. 1870
Attributed to H. CLEMENS of South Dakot
A parody based on the 1849 song "The Ocean Burial
Words by Rev. EDWIN H. CHAPIN
Music by OSSIAN N. DODG

CINDY

Southern Appalachian Folksong

1. You ought to see my
(2.) wish I was an
(3.) wish I had a
(4.) wish I had a
(5.) Cin - dy in the

Cin - dy, she lives a way down south. And She's so sweet the
ap - ple, a - hang - in' on a tree. And ev - 'ry time my
nee - dle, as fine as I could sew. I'd sew that gal to
nick - el, I wish I had a dime. I wish I had my
spring-time, Cin - dy in the fall. If I can't have my

hon - ey bees swarm a - round her mouth.
Cin - dy passed, she'd take a bite of me.
my coat - tail, and down the road I'd go.   Get a - long
Cin - dy girl to love me all the time.
Cin - dy, I'll have no girl at all.

CLEMENTINE

Mining Song, probably from California
Attributed to PERCY MONTROSE
1863 or 1883 (the date is obscured)

1. In a cav - ern, in a can - yon, Ex - ca-
2. was and like a fair - y, And her
3. duck - lings to the wa - ter Ev - 'ry
4. lips a - bove the wa - ter Blow - ing

vat - ing for a mine, Dwelt a min - er, for - ty
shoes were num - ber nine, Her - ring box - es al - with - out a
morn - ing just at nine, Hit her foot a - gainst a was no
bub - bles soft and fine, But, a - las, I

COME ALL YE FAIR AND TENDER MAIDENS

Kentucky Folksong

fair	and ten - der maid - ens,	take warn - ing
(2.) heart	with ten - der sto - ries,	and they'll de -
(3.) out	some night to din - ner,	where can - dles
(4.) wish	I was a spar - row,	and I had
(5.) not	a lit - tle spar - row,	I have no

1. Come all ye

Additional Lyrics

6. Come all ye fair and tender maidens,
   Take warning how you court young men.
   One night they may shine like stars above you,
   To love you that night— but ne'er again.

7. If I had known before he courted,
   That love was such a killing thing,
   I'd a-locked my heart in a chest of iron,
   And tied it down so it couldn't take wing.

COTTON-EYE JOE

Tennessee Folksong

Wistfully

1. Where did you come from, where did you go?
2. Come for to see you, come for to sing,

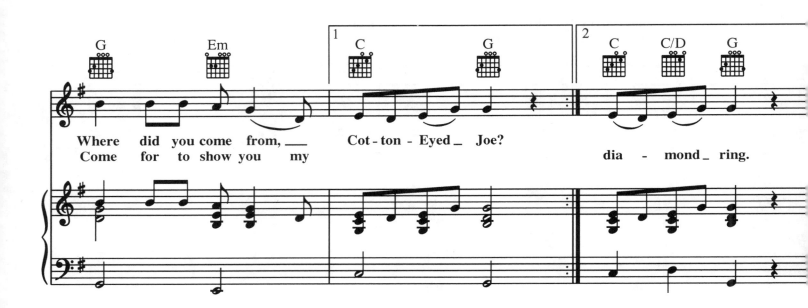

Where did you come from, ___ Cot-ton-Eyed ___ Joe?
Come for to show you my

dia - mond ___ ring.

DOWN IN THE VALLEY

Written by an anonymous
19th century prisoner of
the Raleigh State Prison as a letter
to a girl in Birmingham; the ballad
was published in newspapers across
the country

1. Down in the val - ley,
2. sun - shine,
3. let - ter,

val - ley so low, _____
vi - 'lets love dew, _____
send it by mail; _____

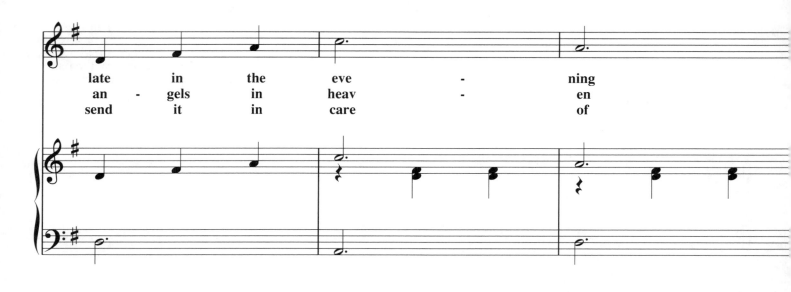

late in the eve - ning
an - gels in heav - en
send it in care of

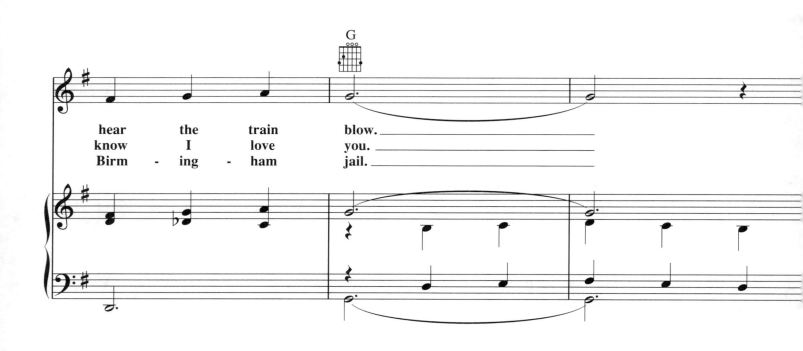

G

hear the train blow.
know I love you.
Birm - ing - ham jail.

Hear that train blow - ing,
Know I love you, dear,
Birm - ing - ham jail - house,

THE CRUEL WAR IS RAGING

American Folkson
from the Civil Wa

THE DRUNKEN SAILOR

American Sea Chante[r]

Moderately fast

Lyrics:

'Way, hay, 'n'up she ris - es! Pat - ent blocks o' diff - 'rent siz - es,

'Way, hay, 'n'up she ris - es Ear - lye in the

Additional Lyrics

Take him an' shake 'im, an' try an' wake i'm,
Earlye in the mornin'!

Give him a dose o' salt an' water,
Earlye in the mornin'!

Give him a taste o' the bosun's rope-end,
Earlye in the mornin'!

THE ERIE CANAL

Anonymous New York Work Song, c. 182
(The Erie Canal, from Albany
Buffalo, opened in 1825

FRANKIE AND JOHNNY

Anonymous Blues Ball
possibly from St. Louis or Kansas C
(There were many versions of the son
with different lovers' names; this
the version that became popula

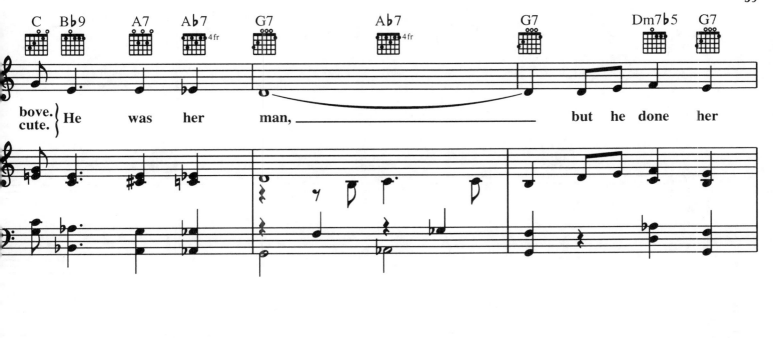

bove.
cute. } He   was   her   man, _____   but   he   done   her

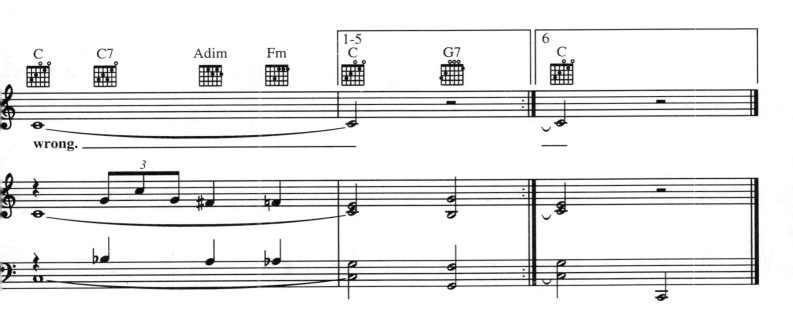

wrong. _____

Additional Lyrics

3. Johnny said, "I've got to leave now,
   But I won't be very long
   Don't sit up and wait for me, honey,
   Don't you worry while I'm gone;"
   He was her man, but he done her wrong.

4. Frankie went down to the hotel,
   Looked in the window so high,
   There she saw her lovin' Johnny
   Making love to Nellie Bly,
   He was her man, but he done her wrong.

5. Johnny saw Frankie a-comin',
   Down the back stairs he did scoot,
   Frankie, she took out her pistol,
   Oh that lady sure could shoot!
   He was her man, but he done her wrong.

6. Frankie, she went to the big chair,
   Calm as a lady could be,
   Turning her eyes up, she whisper'd,
   "Lord, I'm coming up to Thee,
   He was my man, but he done me wrong."

GIT ALONG, LITTLE DOGIES

Western American Cowboy Song

1. As I was a-walk-ing one
2. Ear-ly in spring we round-
3. Whoop-ing and yell-ing and

morn-ing for pleas-ure   I saw a cow-punch-er come
up all the dog-ies.   We mark 'em and brand 'em and
round-ing the dog-ies   from sun-rise till sun-set and

41

HOME ON THE RANGE

Kansas Folksong, c. 1873
possibly written by
DR. BREWSTER HIGLEY (words)
and DAN KELLY (music)

1. Oh, give me a home where the
2. of - ten at night when the
3.,4. *See additional lyrics*

buf - fa - lo roam, where the deer and the
heav - ens are bright, where from the light of the

an - te - lope play, where
glit - ter - ing stars, have I

44

Additional Lyrics

3. Where the air is so pure and the zephyrs so free,
   And the breezes so balmy and light;
   Oh, I would not exchange my home on the range
   For the glittering cities so bright.
   To Chorus

4. Oh, give me a land where the bright diamond sand
   Flows leisurely down with the stream,
   Where the graceful white swan glides slowly along,
   Like a maid in a heavenly dream.
   To Chorus

HIGH BARBAREE

American Sea Chante
sometimes attributed to CHARLES DIBDI

Rollicking

1. There were two loft - y ships from old Eng - land ___
(2.) loft ___ there, a - loft! our ___ jol - ly boat - swain
(3.) naught up - on the stern, there's ___ naught up - on the
(4.) hail ___ her! O hail her! our gal - lant cap - tain
(5.) I am not a man - o' - war or a priv - a - teer," said
6., 7. *(See additional lyrics)*

came,
cries,
lee,"
cried,"
he,

Blow high! Blow low! An' so ___ sailed ___

Additional Lyrics

6. O, 'twas broadside to broadside a long time we lay,
   Blow high! Blow low! An' so sailed we.
   Until the Prince of Luther shot the pirate's masts away.
   All a-cruisin' down the coasts of the High Barbaree!

7. "O quarter! O quarter! those pirates then did cry,
   Blow high! Blow low! An' so sailed we.
   But the quarter that we gave them - we sunk them in the sea.
   All a cruisin' down the coasts of the High Barbaree!

HUSH, LITTLE BABY

Folk Lullaby from the Carolin

THE HOUSE OF THE RISING SUN

Southern American Folksong

50

HOW CAN I KEEP FROM SINGING

American Folk Hymn

I'VE BEEN WORKING ON THE RAILROAD

American Folksong of obsure origin
(It possibly began as a minstrel song
1860-1880, with additions and adaptations)

With Vigor

JESSE JAMES

Anonymous Song from Missou...
about the notorious outlaw, killed in 188...

JOHN HENRY

Anonymous Song from West Virginia, 187(
(John Henry was a railroad steel drive
The legend tells of a contest between Henr
working with a hammer, and a machin
team drill. Henry los

63

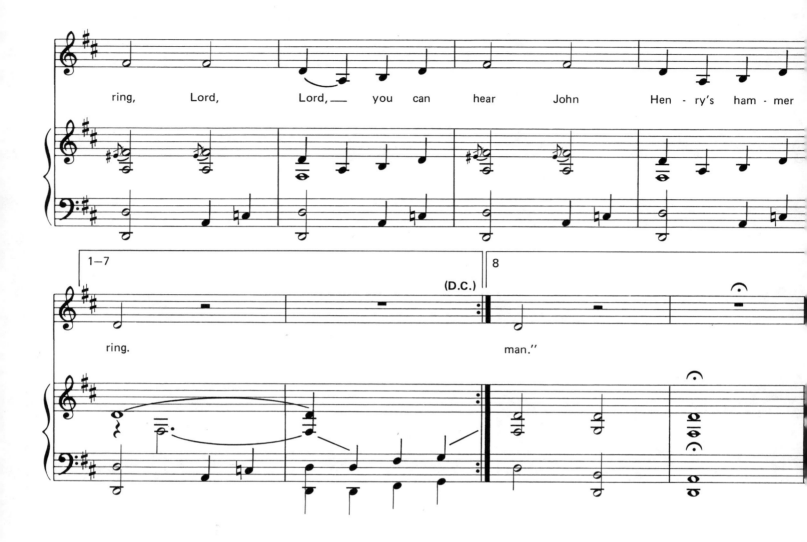

ring, Lord, Lord, ___ you can hear John Hen - ry's ham - mer

ring.

man."

Additional Lyrics

When John Henry was a little baby,
A-sitting on his papa's knee,
He picked up a hammer and a little
     piece of steel,
Said, "Hammer's gonna be the death
     of me". . .

Well, the captain said to John Henry,
"Gonna bring me a steam drill 'round,
Gonna bring me a steam drill out on
     the job,
Gonna whup that steel on down". . .

John Henry said to his captain,
"A man ain't nothin' but a man,
And before I let that steam drill beat
     me down,
I'll die with a hammer in my hand". . .

John Henry said to his shaker,
"Shaker, why don't you pray?
'Cause if I miss this little piece of
     steel,
Tomorrow be your buryin' day. . .

John Henry was driving on the mountain
And his hammer was flashing fire.
And the last words I heard that poor boy
     say,
"Gimme a cool drink of water 'fore I die". . .

John Henry, he drove fifteen feet,
The steam drill only made nine.
But he hammered so hard that he broke
     his poor heart,
And he laid down his hammer and he died. . .

They took John Henry to the graveyard
And they buried him in the sand.
And every locomotive comes a-roaring
     by says,
"There lies a steel-driving man". . .

OLD JOE CLARK

Tennessee Folksong

1. Old Joe Clark, the preach-er's son, preached all o-ver the plain; The
3,5. *(See additional lyrics)*

on-ly text he ev-er used was high low jack and the game.

Chorus

Round and a-round, Old Joe Clark, round and a-round, I say; He'd

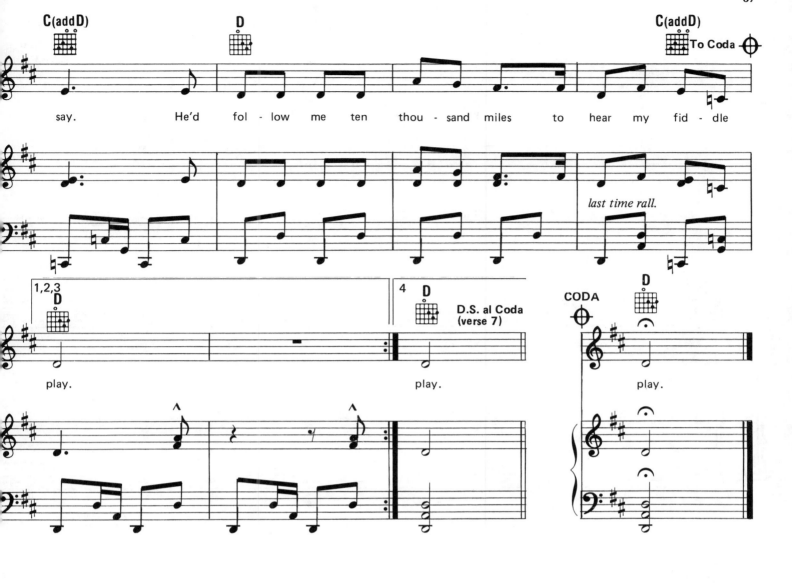

say. He'd fol - low me ten thou - sand miles to hear my fid - dle

last time rall.

play. play. play.

Additional Lyrics

3. When I was a little girl,
   I used to play with toys;
   Now I am a bigger girl,
   I'd rather play with boys. (Chorus)

4. When I was a little boy,
   I used to want a knife;
   Now I am a bigger boy,
   I only want a wife. (Chorus)

5. Wish I was a sugar tree,
   Standin' in the middle of some town;
   Ev'ry time a pretty girl passed,
   I'd shake some sugar down. (Chorus)

6. Old Joe had a yellow cat,
   She would not sing or pray;
   She stuck her head in a buttermilk jar
   And washed her sins away. (Chorus)

7. I wish I had a sweetheart;
   I'd set her on the shelf,
   And ev'ry time she'd smile at me
   I'd get up there myself. (Chorus)

LI'L LIZA JANE

American Folk Ball...
possibly from Maryla...

Additional Lyrics

3. I wouldn't care how far we roam, Li'l Liza Jane,
Where she's at is home sweet home, Li'l Liza Jane.
Oh, Eliza, Li'l Liza Jane!
Oh, Eliza, Li'l Liza Jane

OH! SUSANNA

Words and Music by
STEPHEN COLLINS FOSTER
First published 1848

I come from Al - a - bam - a with my ban - jo on my knee, I'm going to Lou - 'si - an - a, My Su - san - na for to see. It rained all day the

THE OLD CHISHOLM TRAIL

Texas Cowboy Son
(The Chisolm Trail was a cattle driv
route from San Antonio to Dodge City, Kansa
where the herds were sold to market

ON TOP OF OLD SMOKY

Kentucky Mountain Folksong

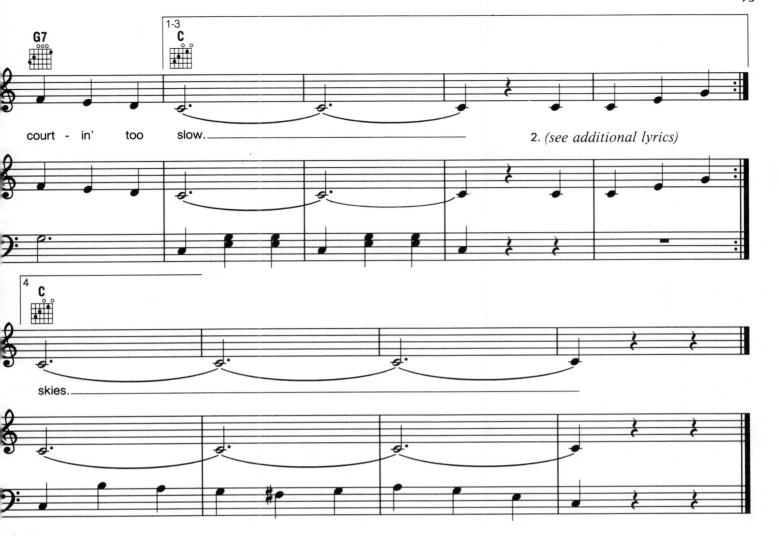

court - in' too slow._____ 2. *(see additional lyrics)*

skies._____

2. A-courtin's a pleasure,
   A-flirtin's a grief,
   A false-hearted lover -
   Is worse than a thief.

3. For a thief, he will rob you,
   And take what you have,
   But a false-hearted lover -
   Sends you to your grave.

4. She'll hug you and kiss you,
   And tell you more lies,
   Than the ties on the railroad,
   Or the stars in the skies.

ONCE I HAD A SWEETHEART

Southern Appalachian Folksong

POLLY WOLLY DOODLE

Traditional American Minstrel Song

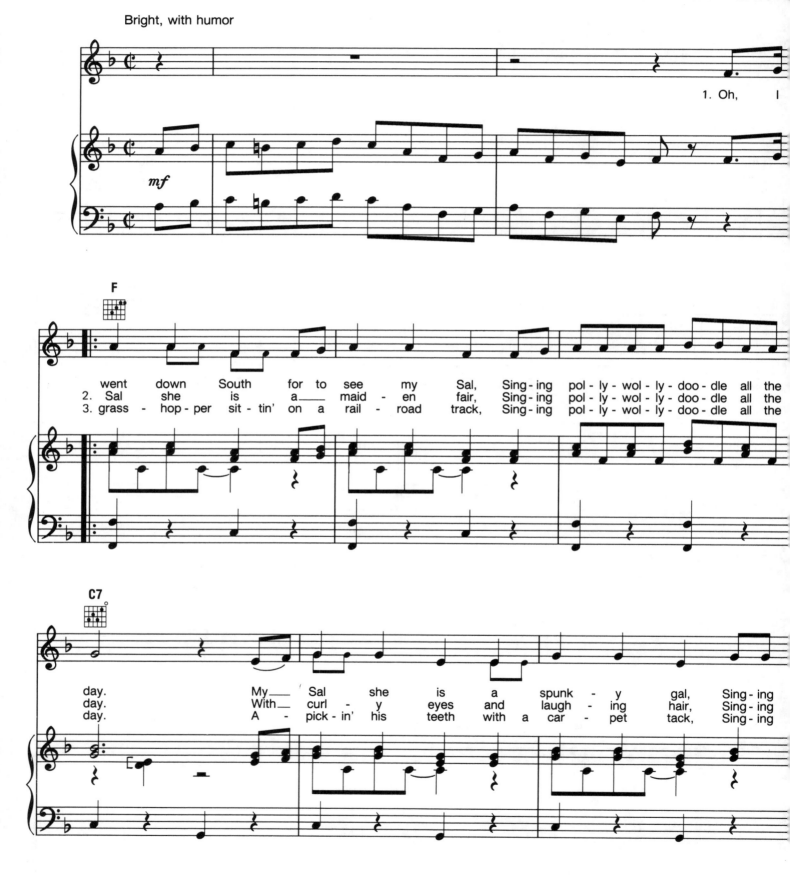

4. Oh, I went to bed, but it wasn't no use,
   Singing polly-wolly-doodle all the day.
   My feet stuck out like a chicken roost,
   Singing polly-wolly-doodle all the day.
   Chorus

5. Behind the barn down on my knees,
   Singing polly-wolly-doodle all the day.
   I thought I heard a chicken sneeze,
   Singing polly-wolly-doodle all the day.
   Chorus

6. He sneezed so hard with the whooping cough,
   Singing polly-wolly-doodle all the day.
   He sneezed his head and tail right off,
   Singing polly-wolly-doodle all the day.
   Chorus

THE RED RIVER VALLEY

Traditional American Cowboy Son
(Believed to be about the valley between Oklahom
and Texas, or alternatively, about the Red Riv
of the North that flows from Minnesota an
the Dakotas to Lake Winnipe

SHENANDOAH

American Folksong
about the Shenandoah Valley of Virginia
(Various versions exist, some about an
Iroquois chief and his daughter; a later, 19th
century sea chantey version was sometimes
sung for weighing anchor.)

SEEING NELLIE HOME

Words by J. FLETCHE
Music by FRANCES KYL
1860

SHE'LL BE COMIN' 'ROUND THE MOUNTAIN

originally a pre-Civil W
African-American Spiritu
"When the Chariot Come
anonymously adapted by eith
mountaineers or rail workers c. 1880s-189
("She" refers to a train locomotiv

Additional Lyrics

3. She'll be wearing red pajamas when she comes...
4. We will all go down to meet her when she comes...
5. We'll be singin' hallelujah when she comes...

SHOO FLY, DON'T BOTHER ME

Nonsense Game Song
the Civil War perio

Moderately fast

Shoo, fly, don't both - er me!

Shoo, fly, don't both - er me! Shoo, fly, don't

both - er me, I be - long to Comp - 'ny G.

To Coda

SHORT'NIN' BREAD

Plantation Song from the American Sou

91

SIMPLE GIFTS

Traditional Shaker Son

93

SKIP TO MY LOU

19th Century American Game Song

2. I'll find another one, prettier than you,
   I'll find another one, prettier than you,
   I'll find another one, prettier than you,
   Skip to my Lou, my darling.

3. Little red wagon, painted blue.

4. Can't get a red bird, a blue bird'll do.

5. Cows in the meadow, moo, moo, moo.

6. Flies in the buttermilk, shoo, shoo, shoo.

SOURWOOD MOUNTAIN

Southern Appalachian Folksong

Moderately fast

1. Chick- ens a- crow-in' on
2. I call my dar- ling a
3. Ducks go a- swim-ming a-

Sour- wood Moun- tain,
blue eyed dais- y,
cross the riv- er,
} Hey! Hey! Dee - dee um day.

So man- y pret- ty girls I can't count 'em,
If she won't have me, I'll sure go cra- zy,
And in the win- ter we sure do shiv- er,
} Hey! Hey! Dee-dee um day.

THE STREETS OF LAREDO

American Cowboy Son[...]
based on the Irish balla[...]
"A Handful of Laure[...]

With a lilt

1. As I _____ walked out in the
(2.) see by your out - fit that
(3.) once in the sad - dle I
(4.) six of my bud - dies to
(5.) beat the drum slow - ly and
6.,7. *(See additional lyrics)*

streets of La - re - do, as I walked
you are a cow - boy", these words he did
used to go dash - ing, with no one as
car - ry my cof - fin, and six pret - ty
play the fife low - ly, and play the dead

out in La - re - do one day, I
say as I calm - ly went by. "Come
quick on the trig - ger as I. I
maid - ens to sing a sad song, take
march as they car - ry my pall. Put

Additional Lyrics

6. "Go gather around you a crowd of young cowboys,
   And tell them the story of this my sad fate.
   Tell one and the other before they go further,
   To stop their wild roving before it's too late."

7. "Go fetch me a cup, just a cup of cold water,
   To cool my parched lips," the cowboy then said.
   Before I returned, his brave spirit had left him,
   And, gone to his Maker, the cowboy was dead.

SWEET BETSY FROM PIKE

American Folksong

Moderately

1. Oh, don't you re-mem-ber sweet
2.-8. *See additional lyrics*

Bet - sy from Pike, who crossed the big moun-tains with her lov - er Ike; with

two yoke of cat - tle, a large yel - low dog, a ___ tall Shang-hai roos - ter, and

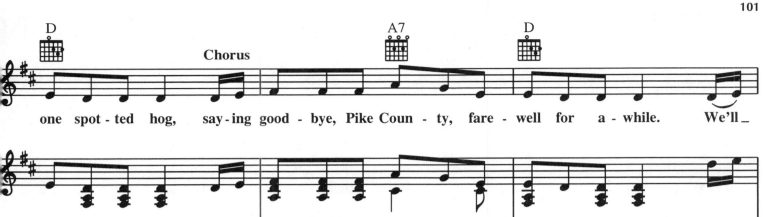

one spot-ted hog, say-ing good-bye, Pike Coun-ty, fare-well for a-while. We'll _

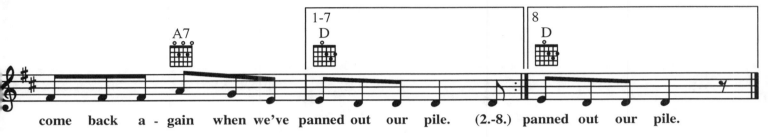

come back a-gain when we've panned out our pile. (2.-8.) panned out our pile.

Additional Lyrics

2. One evening quite early they camped on the Platte,
   'Twas near by the road on a green shady flat,
   Where Betsy, sore-footed, lay down to repose —
   With wonder Ike gazed on that Pike County rose.
   To Chorus

3. Their wagon broke down with a terrible crash,
   And out on the prairie rolled all kinds of trash,
   A few little baby clothes done up with care,
   'Twas rather suspicious, but all on the square.
   To Chorus

4. The Shanghai ran off, and their cattle all died;
   That morning the last piece of bacon was fried;
   Poor Ike was discouraged and Betsy got mad,
   The dog drooped his tail and looked wondrously sad.
   To Chorus

5. They soon reached the desert where Betsy gave out,
   And down in the sand she lay rolling about;
   While Ike, half distracted, looked on with surprise,
   Saying, "Betsy, get up, you'll get sand in your eyes."
   To Chorus

6. Sweet Betsy got up in a great deal of pain,
   Declared she'd go back to Pike County again;
   But Ike gave a sigh, and they fondly embraced,
   And they travelled along with his arm 'round her waist.
   To Chorus

7. They suddenly stopped on a very high hill,
   With wonder looked down upon old Placerville;
   Ike sighed when he said, and he cast his eyes down,
   "Sweet Betsy, my darling, we've got to Hangtown."
   To Chorus

8. Long Ike and sweet Betsy attended a dance;
   Ike wore a pair of his Pike County pants;
   Sweet Betsy was dressed up in ribbons and rings;
   Says Ike, "You're an angel, but where are your wings?"
   To Chorus

THERE IS A TAVERN IN THE TOWN

Drinking Song, originally from Cornwall, England
transcribed by WILLIAM HILLS, 1883

can no long-er stay with you, stay with you,___ I'll ___ hang my

heart on a weep-ing wil-low tree, And may the

world go well with thee. _____ 2. He ___

3. And now I see him nevermore, nevermore.
   He never knocks upon my door, on my door.
   Oh, woe is me, he pinned a little note,
   And these were all the words he wrote:
   (CHORUS)

4. Oh, dig my grave both wide and deep, wide and deep.
   Put tombstones at my head and feet, head and feet.
   And on my breast you may carve a turtle dove,
   To signify I died for love.
   (CHORUS)

THE WABASH CANNON BALL

Hobo Song, c. 1880s

1. From the great At-lan-tic O-cean to the wide Pa-cif-ic's shore, From the ones we leave be-hind us to the ones we see once more. She's
2. Lis-ten to the rhyth-mic jin-gle and the rum-ble and the roar, As she glides a-long the wood-lands thro' the hills and by the shore. You
3. She was com-ing from At-lan-ta on a cold De-cem-ber day. As she rolled in-to the sta-tion, I could hear a wom-an say: "He's

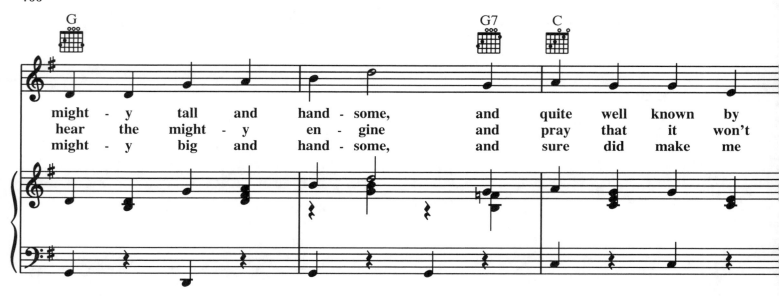

might - y   tall   and   hand - some,   and   quite   well   known   by
hear   the   might - y   en - gine   and   quite   pray   that   it   won't
might - y   big   and   hand - some,   and   sure   did   make   me

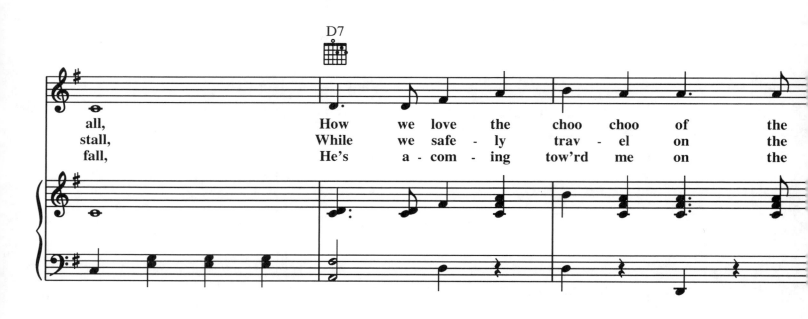

all,   How   we   love   the   choo   choo   of   the
stall,   While   we   safe - ly   trav - el   on   the
fall,   He's   a - com - ing   tow'rd   me   on   the

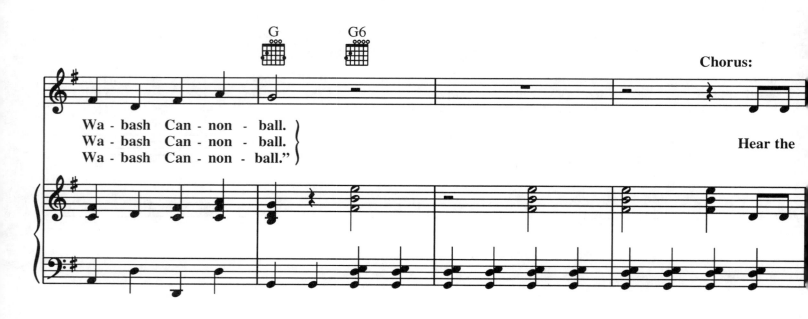

Wa - bash Can - non - ball.)
Wa - bash Can - non - ball. }
Wa - bash Can - non - ball.")

Chorus:

Hear the

TURKEY IN THE STRAW

American Folksong

3. Met Mr. Catfish comin' down stream,
   Says Mr. Catfish, "What does you mean?"
   Caught Mr. Catfish by the snout
   And turned Mr. Catfish wrong side out.
   Chorus:

4. Came to the river and I couldn't get across,
   Paid five dollars for an old blind hoss
   Wouldn't go ahead, nor he wouldn't stand still,
   So he went up and down like an old saw mill.
   Chorus:

5. As I came down the new cut road
   Met Mr. Bullfrog, met Miss Toad,
   And every time Miss Toad would sing
   Ole Bullfrog cut a pigeon wing.
   Chorus:

6. Oh, I jumped in the seat, and I gave a little yell,
   The horses run away, broke the wagon all to hell;
   Sugar in the gourd and honey in the horn,
   I never was so happy since the hour I was born.
   Chorus:

CHORUS
Turkey in the straw, turkey in the hay,
Roll 'em up and twist 'em up a high tuckahaw,
And hit 'em up a tune called Turkey in the Straw.

WHEN JOHNNY COMES MARCHING HOME

Words and Music by LOUIS LAMBERT
pen name for PATRICK GILMORE
written in 1863, melody adapted
from an Irish folksong
(Gilmore was bandmaster of the Union army)

WHEN THE SAINTS GO MARCHING IN

New Orleans Gospel Song
possibly originally from the Bahamas
in 1896 two writers claimed authorship of the song
KATHERINE E. PURVIS (words) and
JAMES M. BLACK (music)

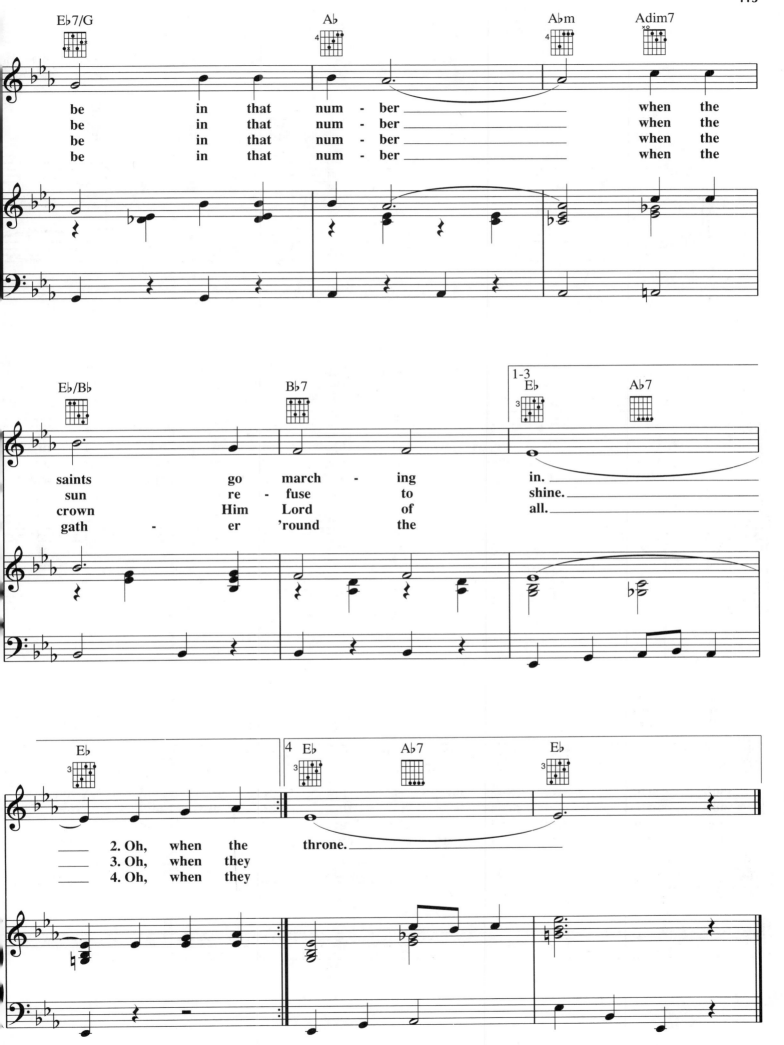

WONDROUS LOVE

Southern American Folk Hymn
17th or 18th centur

YANKEE DOODLE

18th Century Song, possibly originating
with British soldiers of the French and Indian War;
adopted and adapted by American soldiers during
the Revolutionary War

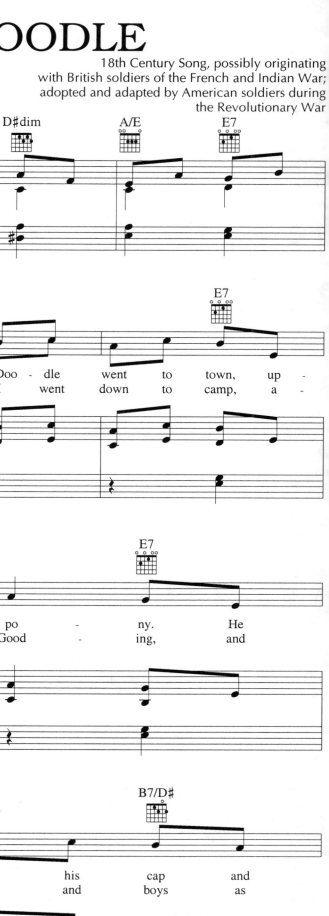

Oh, Yan - kee Doo - dle went to town, up -
Fa - ther and I went down to camp, a -

on a lit - tle po - ny. He
long with Cap - tain Good - ing, He and

stuck a fea - ther in his cap and
there we saw the men and boys as

HE'S GOT THE WHOLE WORLD
IN HIS HANDS

African-American Folksong
possibly from North Carolina

ALL MY TRIALS

African-American Spiritual
from the South

Repeat and Fade

DEEP RIVER

African-American Spiritual
Based on Joshua

DIDN'T MY LORD DELIVER DANIEL?

African-American Spiritual
from the South

129

NOBODY KNOWS THE TROUBLE I'VE SEEN

African-American Spiritual, c. 1850s,
from the islands off
Georgia and South Carolina

EVERY TIME I FEEL THE SPIRIT

African-American Spiritual
from the South

JACOB'S LADDER

African-American Spiritual
from the South, 17th or 18th century

JOSHUA FIT THE BATTLE OF JERICHO

African-American Spiritual
from the South

LET US BREAK BREAD TOGETHER

African-American Spiritual
from the South

Moderately slow

THIS LITTLE LIGHT OF MINE

African-American Spiritual
from the slavery period

THE LONESOME ROAD

African-American Spiritual
c. 1870s-1890s

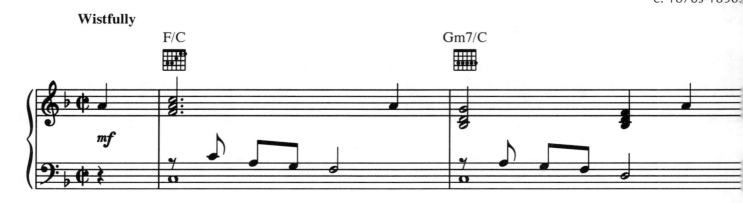

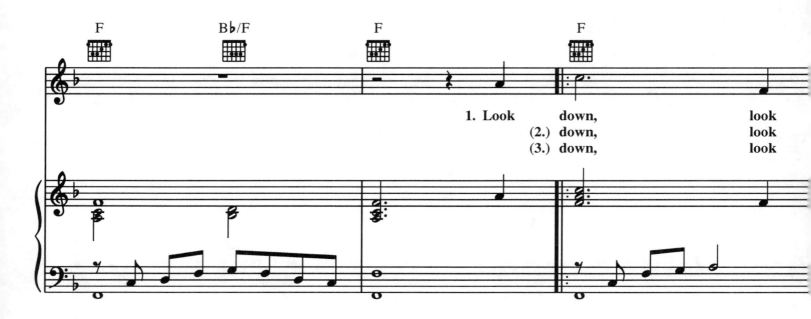

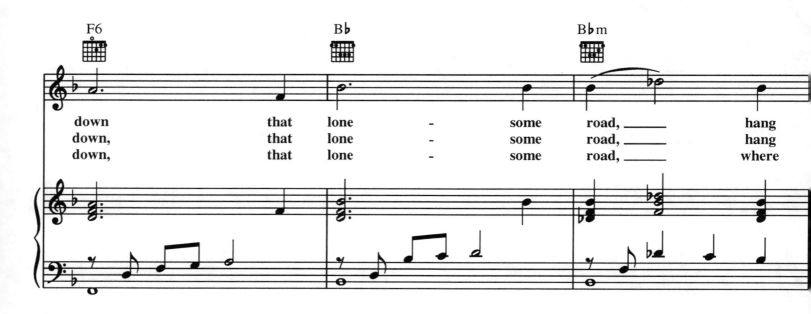

NEVER SAID A MUMBLIN' WORD

African-American Spiritual
from the South

Mournfully

1. Oh, they whipped Him up the hill, _____ up the
(2.) crowned Him with a thorn-y crown, _____ thorn-y
(3.) nailed Him to the cross, _____ to the
(4.) pierced Him in the side, _____ in the
(5.) blood came twink-lin' down, _____ twink-lin'

hill, _____ up the hill, _____ Oh, they whipped Him up the
crown, _____ thorn-y crown, _____ Oh, they crowned Him with a thorn-y
cross, _____ to the cross, _____ Well, they nailed Him to the
side, _____ in the side, _____ Well, they pierced Him in the
down, _____ twink-lin' down, _____ Well, the blood came twink-lin'

OH, FREEDOM

African-American Spiritual
post-Civil War

ROCK-A-MY SOUL

African-American Spiritual
from the slavery period

SOMEBODY'S KNOCKIN' AT YOUR DOOR

African-American Spiritual
from the slavery period

SOMETIMES I FEEL LIKE
A MOTHERLESS CHILD

African-American Spiritual
from the slavery period

SOON AH WILL BE DONE

African-American Spiritua

Soulfully

Soon ah will be done - ah with the

trou - ble of the world, the trou - ble of the world, __ the trou - ble of __ the world.

Soon ah will be done - ah with the trou - ble of the world. Goin' home to live with

STANDING IN THE NEED OF PRAYER

African-American Spiritua[l]

STEAL AWAY

African-American Spiritual
from the slavery period

SWING LOW, SWEET CHARIOT

African-American Spiritual
from the slavery period

THERE IS A BALM IN GILEAD

African-American Spiritual
from the slavery period

WAYFARING STRANGER

Southern American Folk Hymn

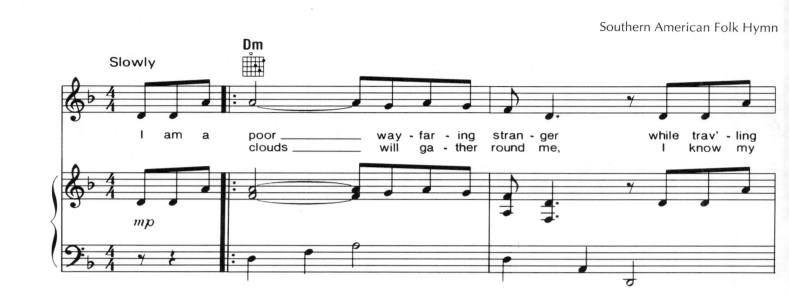

I am a poor _____ way-far-ing stran-ger, while trav'-ling
clouds _____ will ga-ther round me, I know my

through _____ this world of woe, Yet there's no sick - ness, toil nor
way _____ is rough and steep; But gol-den fields _____ lie out be-

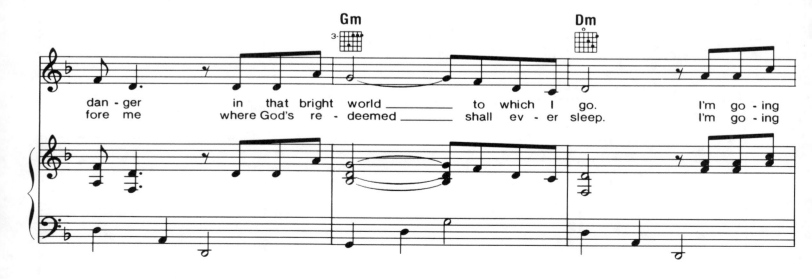

dan-ger in that bright world _____ to which I go. I'm go-ing
fore me where God's re-deemed _____ shall ev-er sleep. I'm go-ing